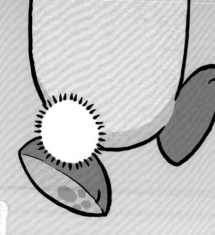

Vern and Lettuce

by Sarah McIntyre

A COLLECTION OF WEEKLY COMIC STRIPS, ORIGINALLY PUBLISHED IN THE DFC.

First published by David Fickling Books 2010

This edition published 2018 by

Bog Eyed Books,
39 coptefield Drive,
Belvedere,
Kent, DA17 5RL

1 3 5 7 9 10 8 6 4 2

Text and Illustrations © 2010 Sarah McIntyre

Printed and bound by comicprintinguk.com

Logo designed by baxterandbailey.co.uk

British Library Cataloguing in Publication Data:
a catalogue record for this book is
available from the British Library

ISBN 978-0-9955553-7-2

bog-eyed-books.com

Jake

Rosie

Clovis

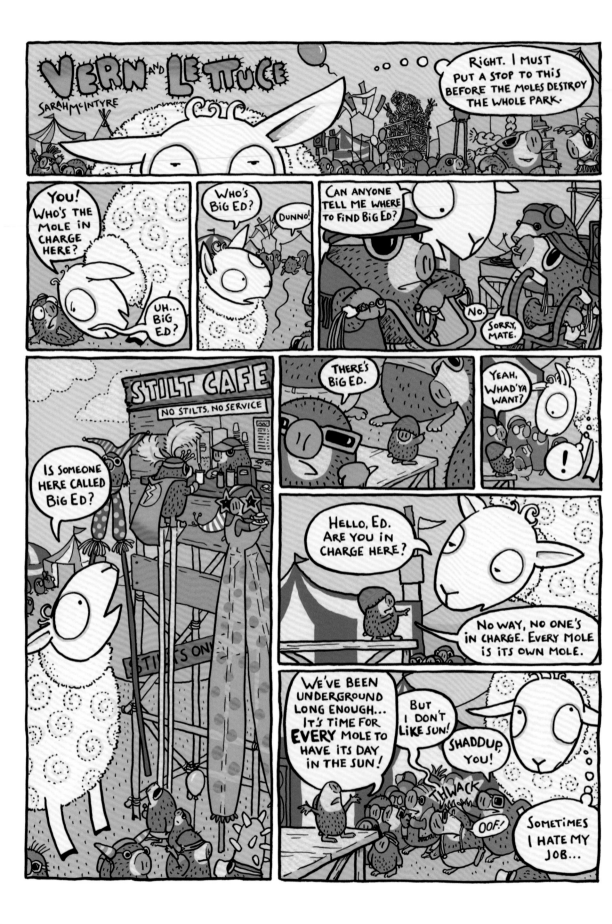

LETTUCE AND VERN'S POP AT FAME

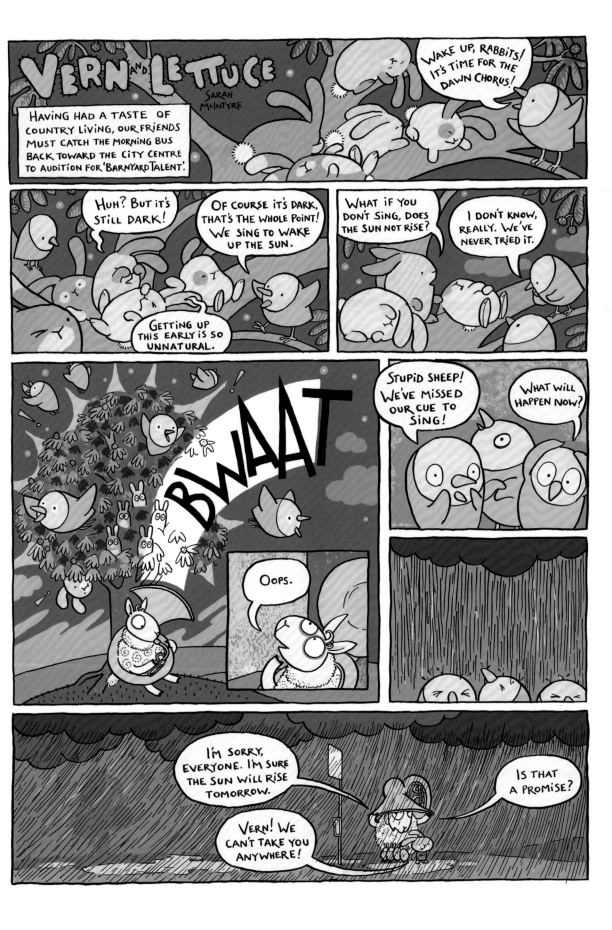

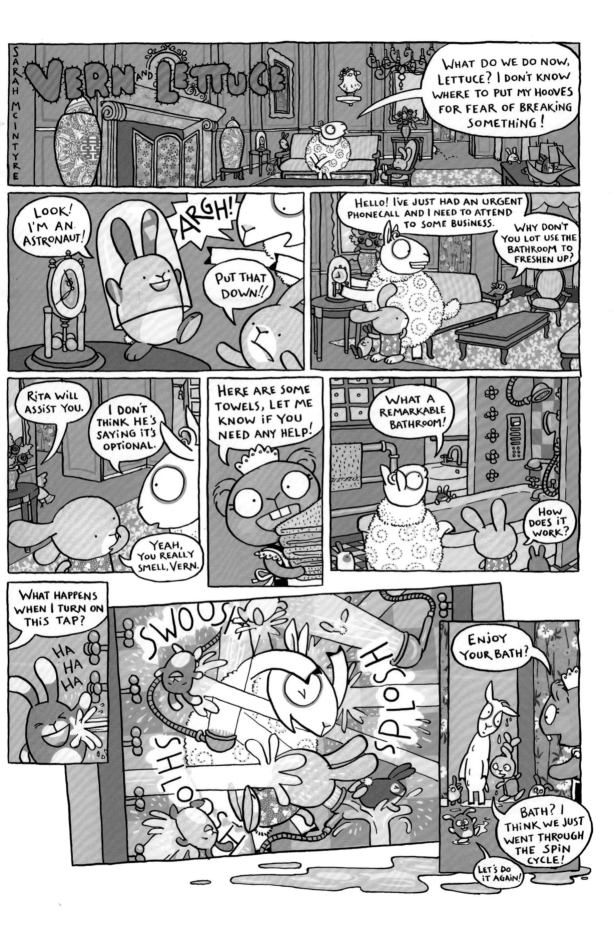

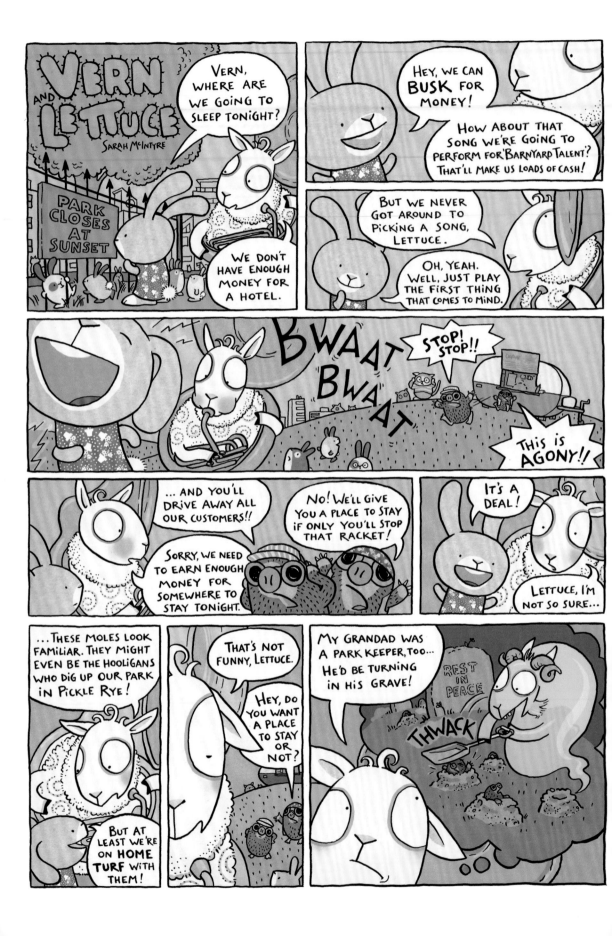

Sarah McIntyre loves making books set in places she knows well, such as her neighbourhood in south London. But then she takes out the people and replaces them with unusual inhabitants. The animal tower block setting inspired the **Vern and Lettuce** comic, and she went on to make a picture book set in the same block, called **The New Neighbours**. She's also created a fictional town for dinosaurs, featured in her picture books **Dinosaur Firefighters** and **Dinosaur Police**.

This comic was originally published as weekly strips in a comic magazine called The DFC, now The Phoenix Comic. She often makes books with her co-author Philip Reeve, and their very first published story together was a four-page comic called **Jinks & O'Hare Funfair Repair** for The Phoenix, which Sarah wrote and Philip illustrated. Later they used that title and setting - an alien funfair planet - and swapped roles to make an illustrated book over 200 pages long. For their books, they still think up stories together, but Philip does most of the writing and Sarah does most of the drawing, on **Roly-Poly Flying Pony: The Legend of Kevin**, **Pugs of the Frozen North**, **Cakes in Space** and **Oliver and the Seawigs**. These books aren't comics, but they often draw short comics about these characters when they're looking for new ideas.

Sarah thinks comics are amazing, because all you need to make them is a pen or pencil and paper, and all you need to publish them is a photocopier or printer. Sarah's first comics were ones she printed and stapled herself, and sold at tables in comics festivals, often with her friend David O'Connell. The two of them went on to create a picture book called **Jampires**, based on a Comic Jam they did together. She hopes lots of kids and grownups alike will be inspired to make and sell their own comics. You can find out more about her and print out activity sheets from her website.

jabberworks.co.uk